Animal Crackers

by **Melissa Schiller**   Illustrated by **Kathleen O'Malley**

Sam and Will are in the store with Mom.

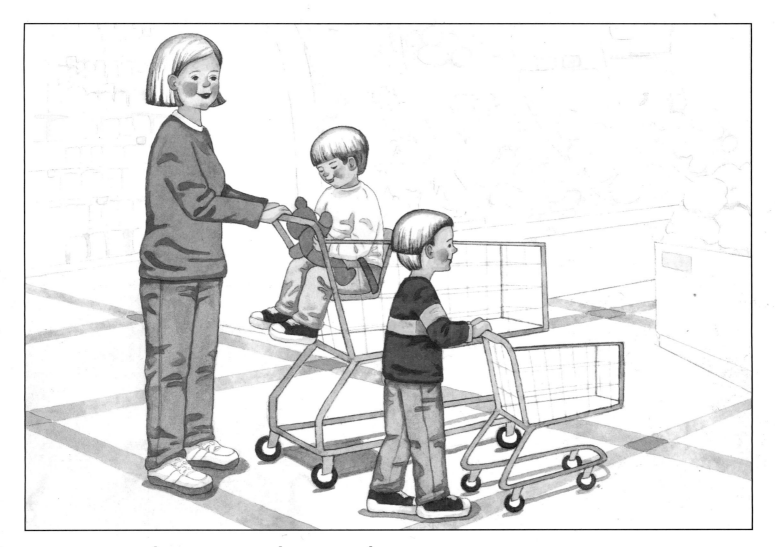

"Mommy has a big shopping cart.
Sam has a little shopping cart," said Will.
"I'm in the big shopping cart."

"Mommy has a box in the big shopping cart. Sam has a box in the little shopping cart, too," said Will.

"Mommy has bread in the big shopping cart. Sam has a zebra in the little shopping cart," said Will.

"Mommy has pretzels in the big shopping cart. Sam has a monkey in the little shopping cart," said Will.

"Mommy has milk in the big shopping cart. Sam has a bear in the little shopping cart," said Will.

"Mommy has carrots in the big shopping cart. Sam has a giraffe in the little shopping cart," said Will.

"Mommy has paper towels in the big shopping cart.

Sam has a lion in the little shopping cart," said Will.

"Mommy has juice in the big shopping cart.
Sam has an elephant in the little shopping cart,"
said Will.

"Zebra, monkey, bear, giraffe, lion, and elephant," said Will.

"Box, bread, pretzels, milk, carrots, paper towels, and juice," said Will.

"Where are the animal crackers?" Mom said.

"Bye!" said Will.